The *Active Reader*

Foundation

Linda Kita-Bradley

Grass Roots Press

Edmonton, Alberta, Canada
2011

The Active Reader – Foundation © 2011 Grass Roots Press

The Active Reader – Foundation is published by

Grass Roots Press
A division of Literacy Services of Canada Ltd.
www.grassrootsbooks.net

AUTHOR   Linda Kita-Bradley
EDITOR   Pat Campbell
DESIGN   Lara Minja
LAYOUT   Susan Hunter

ACKNOWLEDGEMENTS

We acknowledge the financial support of the Government of Canada through the Book Publishing Industry Development Program (BPIDP) for our publishing activities.

We acknowledge the support of the Alberta Foundation for the Arts for our publishing programs.

ISBN 978-1-926583-20-4

Printed in Canada

Contents

About this workbook

Welcome to the Foundation book of *The Active Reader* series. This workbook aims to engage emergent readers in the process of active reading by providing photo stories and activities that develop foundational skills and strategies.

Photo Story

The photo story is introduced with a photo and a pre-reading question, which provides a purpose for reading. The photo story features high-frequency vocabulary and sight words, and repetitive text. Two post-reading questions encourage learners to think about the passage. The first question requires learners to make an inference. The second question requires learners to consider main ideas and details as they discuss the title of the passage. Learners then tell the story in their own words.

Strategies

Letter Names and Sounds

Learners work through a set of activities that introduce a target letter and then reinforce letter-sound relationships.

Predicting Words

Learners predict words by using meaning and/or print clues.

Assisted Reading

With the educator's assistance, learners read the story without the support of photos. When the learners come across unfamiliar words, they are encouraged to use word identification strategies.

Assisted Writing

Learners choose a topic and tell a story. The teacher serves as a scribe and writes down their ideas.

Oh Man!

Letter: M   m

- Look at the picture. What do you see?

- This is Mel.

  What do you think

  Mel is looking for?

- Look at the photo story on pages 2 and 3.

  Your teacher will read the story.

  Find out what Mel is looking for.

Mel is at the store.

Mel gets milk.

He gets eggs.

Mel looks at the meat.

The meat costs so much.

Mel looks in his pocket.

"Oh man!" says Mel.

Mel leaves the milk and eggs.

Mel leaves the store.

▶▶ Talk about the Story

1. Why do you think Mel leaves the milk and eggs?

2. The title of this story is **Oh Man!**

   Explain how the title matches the story.

   Think of a new title for the story.

Read the story again with your teacher.

Then tell the story in your own words.

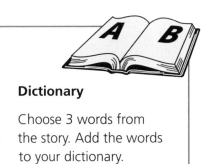

Dictionary

Choose 3 words from the story. Add the words to your dictionary.

Letter Names

Look at the story again.

Circle the words that begin with the letter m.

Choose three of the words. Your teacher will print the words
on the dotted lines. Copy the words on the solid lines.

....

_____   _____   _____

Letters and Sounds

1. Your teacher will read the words in the box.

   The words begin with the letter **m**.

   What sound does the letter **m** make?

   The letter **m** makes the sound /m/.

   Now read the words with your teacher.

Mel	meat
milk	much
man	

2. Think of three more words that begin with the sound /m/.

   Your teacher will print the words.

_____   _____   _____

3. What do you see in each picture?

   Say the word. Then say the first sound of the word.

   Does the word begin with the sound /m/? Circle yes or no.

(a) yes no   (b) yes no   (c) yes no

Predict Words

Your teacher will read each sentence.

Sound out the first letter of the missing word.

Then say a word that makes sense. Your teacher will print the word.

1. May is the best m_____ of the year.

2. Women and m_____ play hockey.

3. Spring starts in the month of M_____ .

Now read each sentence with your teacher.

Assisted Reading

Read the story below with your teacher.

Is a word hard to read?
Active readers use these strategies:

- Sound out the first letter.
- Think of a word that makes sense.
- Ask someone for help.
- Skip the word.

Oh Man!

Mel is at the store.

Mel gets milk.

He gets eggs.

Mel looks at the meat.

The meat costs so much.

Mel looks in his pocket.

"Oh man!" says Mel.

Mel leaves the milk and eggs.

Mel leaves the store.

Assisted Writing

1. Choose a topic from the box.
   Tell a story about it.

2. Watch your words turn into print.
   Your teacher will write down your story.

- A time you forgot something

- The first time you bought something with your own money

Good Food, Bad Food

Letter: F   f

- Look at the picture. What do you see?

- This is Fay and Mac.

  Fay makes lunch for Mac.

  Why do you think

  Mac looks sad?

- Look at the photo story on pages 8 and 9.

  Your teacher will read the story.

  Find out why Mac looks sad.

Fay makes lunch for Mac.

Mac eats the salad.

Yuck! The salad has eggs.

Mac eats the fish.

Yuck! The fish has too much lemon.

Mac eats the fries.

Yuck! The fries have too much salt.

Fay says, "How is the food?"

Mac says, "Very, very good."

▶▶ Talk about the Story

1. Why do you think Mac says the food is good?

2. The title of this story is **Good Food, Bad Food**.

Explain how the title matches the story.

Think of a new title for the story.

Read the story again with your teacher.

Then tell the story in your own words.

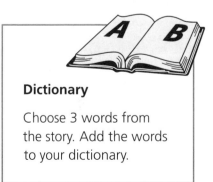

Dictionary

Choose 3 words from the story. Add the words to your dictionary.

Letter Names

Look at the story again.

Circle the words that begin with the letter f.

Choose three of the words. Your teacher will print the words
on the dotted lines. Copy the words on the solid lines.

....

_____   _____   _____

Letters and Sounds

1. Your teacher will read the words in the box.

   The words begin with the letter **f**.

   What sound does the letter **f** make?

   The letter **f** makes the sound /f/.

   Now read the words with your teacher.

Fay	fish
food	

In some words, the
letters **ph** make
the sound /f/.

phone   photo

2. Think of three more words that begin with

   the sound /f/. Your teacher will print the words.

_____   _____   _____

3. What do you see in each picture?

Say the word. Then say the first sound of the word.

Does the word begin with the sound /f/? Circle yes or no.

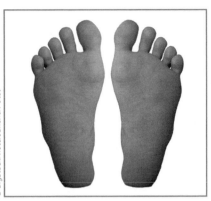

(a) yes no

(b) yes no

(c) yes no

Predict Words

Your teacher will read each sentence.

Sound out the first letter of the missing word.

Then say a word that makes sense. Your teacher will print the word.

1. He can run very f_____ .

2. I took the kids to the park. We had f_____ .

3. She has two dogs and f_____ cats.

Now read each sentence with your teacher.

Assisted Reading

**Read the story below
with your teacher.**

Is a word hard to read?
Active readers use these strategies:

- Sound out the first letter.
- Think of a word that makes sense.
- Ask someone for help.
- Skip the word.

Good Food, Bad Food

Fay makes lunch for Mac.

Mac eats the salad.

Yuck! The salad has eggs.

Mac eats the fish.

Yuck! The fish has too much lemon.

Mac eats the fries.

Yuck! The fries have too much salt.

Fay says, "How is the food?"

Mac says, "Very, very good."

Assisted Writing

1. Choose a topic from the box.
   Tell a story about it.

2. Watch your words turn into print.
   Your teacher will write down your story.

- A time you
  ate something
  you did not like

- A time you told a white lie

No Time

Letter: T t

- Look at the picture. What do you see?

- This is Tess.

  What do you think

  Tess is going to do?

- Look at the photo story on pages 14 and 15.

  Your teacher will read the story.

  Find out why Tess looks sad.

Tess needs to clean up.

But first Tess makes tea.

She talks on the phone.

She talks and talks.

Tess watches TV.

She makes a sandwich.

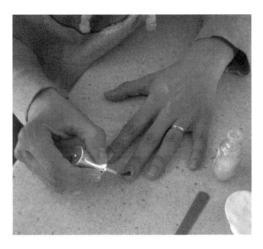

Tess does her nails.

What! Ten o'clock!

Tess goes to bed.

▶▶ Talk about the Story

1. Describe Tess in your own words.

2. The title of this story is **No Time**.

Explain how the title matches the story.

Think of a new title for the story.

Read the story again with your teacher.

Then tell the story in your own words.

Dictionary

Choose 3 words from the story. Add the words to your dictionary.

Letter Names

Look at the story again.

Circle the words that begin with the letter t.

Choose three of the words. Your teacher will print the words on the dotted lines. Copy the words on the solid lines.

....

_____   _____   _____

Letters and Sounds

1. Your teacher will read the words in the box.

    The words begin with the letter **t**.

    What sound does the letter **t** make?

    The letter **t** makes the sound /t/.

    Now read the words with your teacher.

2. Think of three more words that begin with the sound /t/.

    Your teacher will print the words.

_____   _____   _____

3. What do you see in each picture?

   Say the word. Then say the first sound of the word.

   Does the word begin with the sound /t/? Circle yes or no.

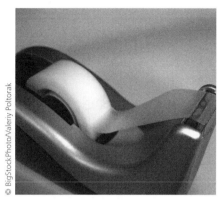

(a) yes no   (b) yes no   (c) yes no

Predict Words

Your teacher will read each sentence.

Sound out the first letter of the missing word.

Then say a word that makes sense. Your teacher will print the word.

1. Don't t_____ me what to do.

2. My son is t_____ years old.

3. Slow down. T_____ your time.

Now read each sentence with your teacher.

Assisted Reading

**Read the story below
with your teacher.**

No Time

Tess needs to clean up.

But first Tess makes tea.

She talks on the phone.

She talks and talks.

Tess watches TV.

She makes a sandwich.

Tess does her nails.

What! Ten o'clock!

Tess goes to bed.

Is a word hard to read?
Active readers use these strategies:

- Sound out the first letter.

- Think of a word that makes sense.

- Ask someone for help.

- Skip the word.

Assisted Writing

1. Choose a topic from the box.
   Tell a story about it.

2. Watch your words turn into print.
   Your teacher will write down your story.

- A time you put off
  doing something

- A time you were late
  for something

A Bad Dream

Letter: B b

- Look at the picture. What do you see?

- This is Bud.

  Why do you think

  Bud looks afraid?

- Look at the photo story on pages 20 and 21.

  Your teacher will read the story.

  Find out why Bud looks afraid.

Bud washes a jar.

Oh oh! Bud's hand is stuck.

Bud cannot get his hand out.

Bud's wife helps.

But Bud's hand is still stuck.

Bud's wife gets a hammer.

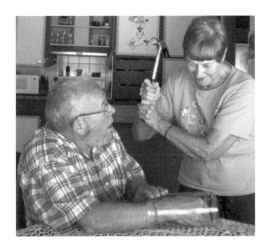

She wants to break the jar.

Bud yells, "NO!"

Bud wakes up.

▶▶ Talk about the Story

1. How do you think Bud feels when he wakes up?

2. The title of this story is **A Bad Dream**.

   Explain how the title matches the story.

   Think of a new title for the story.

Read the story again with your teacher.

Then tell the story in your own words.

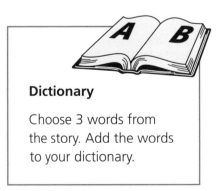

Dictionary

Choose 3 words from the story. Add the words to your dictionary.

Letter Names

Look at the story again.

Circle the words that begin with the letter b.

Choose three of the words. Your teacher will print the words on the dotted lines. Copy the words on the solid lines.

....

_____   _____   _____

Letters and Sounds

1. Your teacher will read the words in the box.

    The words begin with the letter **b**.

    What sound does the letter **b** make?

Bud	bad
but	

    The letter **b** makes the sound /b/.

    Now read the words with your teacher.

2. Think of three more words that begin with the sound /b/.

    Your teacher will print the words.

_____   _____   _____

3. What do you see in each picture?

   Say the word. Then say the first sound of the word.

   Does the word begin with the sound /b/? Circle yes or no.

 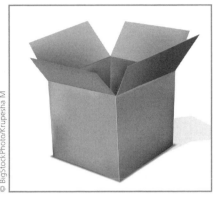 

(a) yes no   (b) yes no   (c) yes no

Predict Words

Your teacher will read each sentence.

Sound out the first letter of the missing word.

Then say a word that makes sense. Your teacher will print the word.

1. I ride a b_____ to work.

2. I picked up the box. I hurt my b_____ .

3. This is the b_____ movie I have ever seen.

Now read each sentence with your teacher.

Assisted Reading

Read the story below with your teacher.

A Bad Dream

Bud washes out a jar.

Oh oh! Bud's hand is stuck.

Bud cannot get his hand out.

Bud's wife helps.

But Bud's hand is still stuck.

Bud's wife gets a hammer.

She wants to break the jar.

Bud yells, "NO!"

Bud wakes up.

Is a word hard to read?
Active readers use these strategies:

- Sound out the first letter.
- Think of a word that makes sense.
- Ask someone for help.
- Skip the word.

Assisted Writing

1. Choose a topic from the box.
   Tell a story about it.

2. Watch your words turn into print.
   Your teacher will write down your story.

My Words

- A dream you have had more than once

- A time you helped someone

Lost and Found

Letter: L   l

- Look at the picture. What do you see?

- This is Lin.

  Why do you think

  Lin is laughing?

- Look at the photo story on pages 26 and 27.

  Your teacher will read the story.

  Find out why Lin is laughing.

Lin needs her glasses.

Lin looks on her desk.

She looks in her purse.

She looks in her coat pocket.

She looks in the lunchroom.

Lin looks in one last place.

Lin looks in the bathroom.

Then Lin looks up.

Lin starts to laugh.

▶▶ Talk about the Story

1. How do you think Lin feels when she finds her glasses?

2. The title of this story is **Lost and Found**.

Explain how the title matches the story.

Think of a new title for the story.

Read the story again with your teacher.

Then tell the story in your own words.

Dictionary

Choose 3 words from the story. Add the words to your dictionary.

Letter Names

Look at the story again.

Circle the words that begin with the letter l.

Choose three of the words. Your teacher will print the words on the dotted lines. Copy the words on the solid lines.

....

_____   _____   _____

Letters and Sounds

1. Your teacher will read the words in the box.

    The words begin with the letter l.

    What sound does the letter l make?

    The letter l makes the sound /l/.

    Now read the words with your teacher.

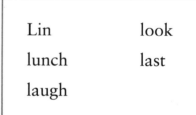

Lin   look

lunch   last

laugh

2. Think of three more words that begin with the sound /l/.

    Your teacher will print the words.

_____   _____   _____

3. What do you see in each picture?

Say the word. Then say the first sound of the word.

Does the word begin with the sound /l/? Circle yes or no.

(a) yes no   (b) yes no   (c) yes no

Predict Words

Your teacher will read each sentence.

Sound out the first letter of the missing word.

Then say a word that makes sense. Your teacher will print the word.

1. I do not l_____ to cook.

2. Go away! L_____ me alone!

3. We l_____ in a big city.

Now read each sentence with your teacher.

Assisted Reading

**Read the story below
with your teacher.**

Lost and Found

Lin needs her glasses.

Lin looks on her desk.

She looks in her purse.

She looks in her coat pocket.

She looks in the lunchroom.

Lin looks in one last place.

Lin looks in the bathroom.

Then Lin looks up.

Lin starts to laugh.

Is a word hard to read?
Active readers use these strategies:

- Sound out the first letter.

- Think of a word that makes sense.

- Ask someone for help.

- Skip the word.

Assisted Writing

1. Choose a topic from the box.
   Tell a story about it.

2. Watch your words turn into print.
   Your teacher will write down your story.

- A time you lost
  something

- A time you did
  something silly

My Dear Son

Letter: D d

- Look at the picture. What do you see?

- This is Dan.

    Dan drives his dad crazy.

    Why do you think

    Dan drives his dad crazy?

- Look at the photo story on pages 32 and 33.

    Your teacher will read the story.

    Find out why Dan drives his dad crazy.

Dan is my son.

Dan talks on the phone all day.

He watches TV all night.

He sleeps till noon.

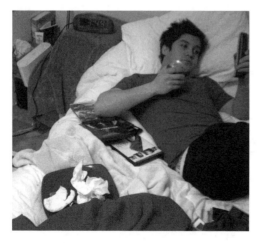

Dan does not clean his room.

He does not take out the garbage.

He does not do dishes.

Dan drives me crazy.

But I love him to death.

▶▶ Talk about the Story

1. Describe Dan's dad in your own words.

2. The title of this story is **My Dear Son**.
Explain how the title matches the story.
Think of a new title for the story.

Read the story again with your teacher.
Then tell the story in your own words.

Dictionary

Choose 3 words from the story. Add the words to your dictionary.

Letter Names

Look at the story again.

Circle the words that begin with the letter d.

Choose three of the words. Your teacher will print the words on the dotted lines. Copy the words on the solid lines.

....

_____   _____   _____

Letters and Sounds

1. Your teacher will read the words in the box.

    The words begin with the letter **d**.

    What sound does the letter **d** make?

    The letter **d** makes the sound /d/.

    Now read the words with your teacher.

Dan	day
does	do
dish	death
dear	

2. Think of three more words that begin with the sound /d/.

    Your teacher will print the words.

_____   _____   _____

3. What do you see in each picture?

Say the word. Then say the first sound of the word.

Does the word begin with the sound /d/? Circle yes or no.

(a) yes no   (b) yes no   (c) yes no

Predict Words

Your teacher will read each sentence.

Sound out the first letter of the missing word.

Then say a word that makes sense. Your teacher will print the word.

1. The cost of food goes up, not d_____ .

2. Turn up the music. Let's d_____ .

3. Today's _____ is May 9.

Now read each sentence with your teacher.

Assisted Reading

**Read the story below
with your teacher.**

Is a word hard to read?
Active readers use these strategies:

- Sound out the first letter.
- Think of a word that makes sense.
- Ask someone for help.
- Skip the word.

My Dear Son

Dan is my son.

Dan talks on the phone all day.

He watches TV all night.

He sleeps till noon.

Dan does not clean his room.

He does not take out the garbage.

He does not do dishes.

Dan drives me crazy.

But I love him to death.

Assisted Writing

1. Choose a topic from the box.
   Tell a story about it.

2. Watch your words turn into print.
   Your teacher will write down your story.

- A person that
  drives you crazy

- A person that
  you love to death

A Nice Day

Letter: N n

- Look at the picture. What do you see?

- This is Nan.

  Nan sees a note on her fridge.

  What do you think the note says?

- Look at the photo story on pages 38 and 39.

  Your teacher will read the story.

  Find out what the note says.

Nan goes to the store.

The store is closed.

Nan needs some money.

The ATM is out of order.

Nan sits down to rest.

Nan sits on wet paint.

Nan goes home.

Nan sees a note.

The note says, "I love you."

►► Talk about the Story

1. What do you think Nan will remember about this day?

2. The title of this story is **A Nice Day**.

   Explain how the title matches the story.

   Think of a new title for the story.

Read the story again with your teacher.

Then tell the story in your own words.

Dictionary

Choose 3 words from the story. Add the words to your dictionary.

Letter Names

Look at the story again.

Circle the words that begin with the letter n.

Your teacher will print the words on the dotted lines.

Copy the words on the solid lines.

....

_____   _____   _____

Letters and Sounds

1. Your teacher will read the words in the box.

   The words begin with the letter **n**.

   What sound does the letter **n** make?

Nan	nice
need	note

   The letter **n** makes the sound /n/.

   Now read the words with your teacher.

2. Think of three more words that begin with the sound /n/.

   Your teacher will print the words.

_____   _____   _____

3. What do you see in each picture?

   Say the word. Then say the first sound of the word.

   Does the word begin with the sound /n/? Circle yes or no.

 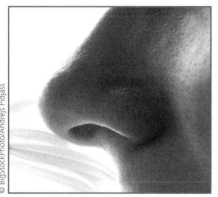 

(a) yes no   (b) yes no   (c) yes no

Predict Words

Your teacher will read each sentence.

Sound out the first letter of the missing word.

Then say a word that makes sense. Your teacher will print the word.

1. It can snow in the month of N_____ .

2. I go to bed late every n_____ .

3. Her first n_____ is Nan.

Now read each sentence with your teacher.

Assisted Reading

**Read the story below
with your teacher.**

A Bad Dream

Nan goes to the store.

The store is closed.

Nan needs some money.

The ATM is out of order.

Nan sits down to rest.

Nan sits on wet paint.

Nan goes home.

Nan sees a note.

The note says, "I love you."

Is a word hard to read?
Active readers use these strategies:

- Sound out the first letter.

- Think of a word that makes sense.

- Ask someone for help.

- Skip the word.

Assisted Writing

1. Choose a topic from the box.
   Tell a story about it.

2. Watch your words turn into print.
   Your teacher will write down your story.

- A nice surprise

- A day when nothing
  went right

Pay Day

Letter: P p

- Look at the picture. What do you see?

- This is Pam.

  What do you think

  Pam is looking for?

- Look at the photo story on pages 44 and 45.

  Your teacher will read the story.

  Find out what Pam is looking for.

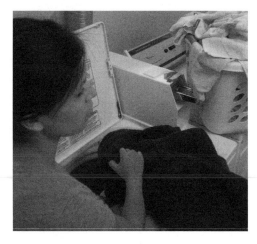

Pam has to wash clothes.

Pam picks up a pair of pants.

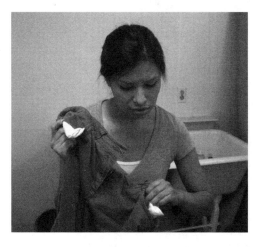

She looks in the pocket.

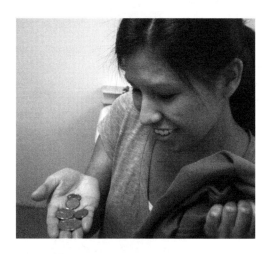

Pam finds money.

Pam picks up a jacket.

She looks in the pocket.

Pam finds more money.

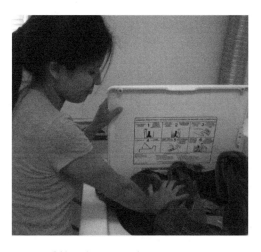

Pam fills the washer.

Then Pam goes for coffee.

▶▶ Talk about the Story

1. Do you think Pam made good use of her money?

2. The title of this story is **Pay Day**.

Explain how the title matches the story.

Think of a new title for the story.

Read the story again with your teacher.

Then tell the story in your own words.

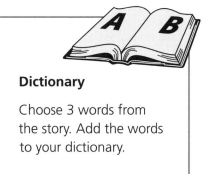

Dictionary

Choose 3 words from the story. Add the words to your dictionary.

Letter Names

Look at the story again.

Circle the words that begin with the letter p.

Choose three of the words. Your teacher will print the words on the dotted lines. Copy the words on the solid lines.

....

_____   _____   _____

Letters and Sounds

1. Your teacher will read the words in the box.

   The words begin with the letter **p**.

   What sound does the letter **p** make?

   The letter **p** makes the sound /p/.

   Now read the words with your teacher.

Pam	pick
pair	pants
pocket	pay

2. Think of three more words that begin with the sound /p/.

   Your teacher will print the words.

_____   _____   _____

3. What do you see in each picture?

   Say the word. Then say the first sound of the word.

   Does the word begin with the sound /p/? Circle yes or no.

(a) yes no   (b) yes no   (c) yes no

Predict Words

Your teacher will read each sentence.

Sound out the first letter of the missing word.

Then say a word that makes sense. Your teacher will print the word.

1. I need new pots and p_____ .

2. The form says to p_____ your name.

3. I got some stamps at the p_____ office.

Now read each sentence with your teacher.

Assisted Reading

**Read the story below
with your teacher.**

Pay Day

Pam has to wash clothes.

Pam picks up a pair of pants.

She looks in the pocket.

Pam finds money.

Pam picks up a jacket.

She looks in the pocket.

Pam finds more money.

Pam fills the washer.

Then Pam goes for coffee.

Is a word hard to read?
Active readers use these strategies:

- Sound out the first letter.

- Think of a word that makes sense.

- Ask someone for help.

- Skip the word.

Assisted Writing

1. Choose a topic from the box.
   Tell a story about it.

2. Watch your words turn into print.
   Your teacher will write down your story.

- A time you found
  some money

- A time you gave
  yourself a treat

Bus Stop

Letter: S s

- Look at the picture. What do you see?

- Look at the picture.

  Why do you think the man

  is looking at the woman?

- Look at the photo story on pages 50 and 51.

  Your teacher will read the story.

  Find out why the man is looking at the woman.

The man and woman wait for the bus.

The woman looks at the man.

The man looks at the woman.

The woman smiles.

The man smiles.

The bus comes.

The bus stops.

The bus goes.

The man sits down.

▶▶ Talk about the Story

1. Why do you think the man and woman do not get on the bus?

2. The title of this story is **Bus Stop**. Explain how the title matches the story. Think of a new title for the story.

Read the story again with your teacher.

Then tell the story in your own words.

Dictionary

Choose 3 words from the story. Add the words to your dictionary.

Letter Names

Look at the story again.

Circle the words that begin with the letter s.

Your teacher will print the words on the dotted lines.

Copy the words on the solid lines.

....

_____   _____   _____

Letters and Sounds

1. Your teacher will read the words in the box.

   The words begin with the letter s.

   What sound does the letter s make?

   The letter s makes the sound /s/.

   Now read the words with your teacher.

| sit | stop |
| smile | |

In some words, the letter c makes the sound /s/.

| city | circle |
| centre | cereal |

2. Think of three more words that begin with the sound /s/. Your teacher will print the words.

_____   _____   _____

3. What do you see in each picture?

Say the word. Then say the first sound of the word.

Does the word begin with the sound /s/? Circle yes or no.

(a) yes no   (b) yes no   (c) yes no

Predict Words

Your teacher will read each sentence.

Sound out the first letter of the missing word.

Then say a word that makes sense. Your teacher will print the word.

1. The best day of the week is S_____ .

2. I had a bowl of s_____ for lunch.

3. Repeat that. What did you s_____ ?

Now read each sentence with your teacher.

Assisted Reading

**Read the story below
with your teacher.**

Bus Stop

The man and woman wait for the bus.

The woman looks at the man.

The man looks at the woman.

The woman smiles.

The man smiles.

The bus comes.

The bus stops.

The bus goes.

The man sits down.

Is a word hard to read?
Active readers use these strategies:

- Sound out the first letter.

- Think of a word that makes sense.

- Ask someone for help.

- Skip the word.

Assisted Writing

1. Choose a topic from the box.
   Tell a story about it.

2. Watch your words turn into print.
   Your teacher will write down your story.

- Falling in love
  at first sight

- A time you took
  a chance on something

Holey Socks

Letter: H   h

- Look at the picture. What do you see?

- This is Hal.

  Why do you think

  Hal looks so pleased?

- Look at the photo story on pages 56 and 57.

  Your teacher will read the story.

  Find out why Hal looks so pleased.

Hal needs new socks.

Hal goes to the store.
Wow! Good sale!

Hal buys a pair of pants.

He buys a T-shirt.

He buys a hat.

Hal goes home.

Hal puts on his new clothes.

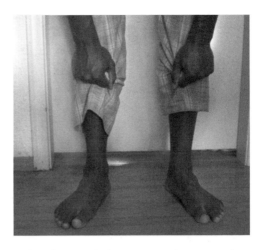

Oh oh! Hal forgot to buy socks.

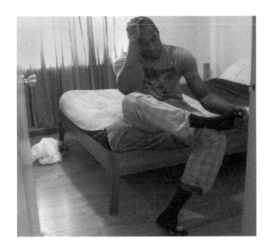

Darn! Hal must wear holey socks.

▶▶ Talk about the Story

1. Why do you think Hal forgot to buy socks?

2. The title of this story is **Holey Socks**.

Explain how the title matches the story.

Think of a new title for the story.

Read the story again with your teacher.

Then tell the story in your own words.

Dictionary

Choose 3 words from the story. Add the words to your dictionary.

Letter Names

Look at the story again.

Circle the words that begin with the letter h.

Choose three of the words. Your teacher will print the words
on the dotted lines. Copy the words on the solid lines.

....

_____   _____   _____

Letters and Sounds

1. Your teacher will read the words in the box.

    The words begin with the letter **h**.

    What sound does the letter **h** make?

Hal	hat
home	hole

    The letter **h** makes the sound /h/.

    Now read the words with your teacher.

2. Think of three more words that begin with the sound /h/.

    Your teacher will print the words.

_____   _____   _____

3. What do you see in each picture?

Say the word. Then say the first sound of the word.

Does the word begin with the sound /h/? Circle yes or no.

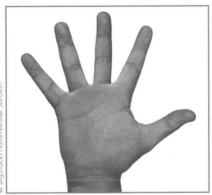

(a) yes no   (b) yes no   (c) yes no

Predict Words

Your teacher will read each sentence.

Sound out the first letter of the missing word.

Then say a word that makes sense. Your teacher will print the word.

1. Hello. H_____ are you?

2. Say that again. I did not h_____ you.

3. Are you okay? Do you need h_____ ?

Now read each sentence with your teacher.

Assisted Reading

**Read the story below
with your teacher.**

Is a word hard to read?
Active readers use these strategies:

- Sound out the first letter.

- Think of a word that makes sense.

- Ask someone for help.

- Skip the word.

Holey Socks

Hal needs new socks.

Hal goes to the store.

Wow! Good sale!

Hal buys a pair of pants.

He buys a T-shirt.

He buys a hat.

Hal goes home.

Hal puts on his new clothes.

Oh oh! Hal forgot to buy socks.

Darn! Hal must wear holey socks.

Assisted Writing

1. Choose a topic from the box.
   Tell a story about it.

2. Watch your words turn into print.
   Your teacher will write down your story.

- A time you found
  a good buy

- Your favourite
  piece of clothing

ANSWER KEY

In some cases, the answer key contains only a few of the possible responses for questions. There are other acceptable responses for these questions.

Unit 1: Oh Man!

Talk about the Story: 1. Mel forgot to bring money to the store. **2.** Mel says "oh man" when he realizes he forgot to bring his money. Mel says "oh man" because he is annoyed with himself for forgetting his money.

Letters and Sounds: 3a. no: heart **3b.** yes: moon **3c.** yes: mask

Predict Words: Possible responses: **1.** month **2.** men **3.** March

Unit 2: Good Food, Bad Food

Talk about the Story: 1. Mac does not want to hurt Fay's feelings. **2.** Mac thinks the food is bad, but he says it is good.

Letters and Sounds: 3a. yes: fork **3b.** yes: feet **3c.** no: mug

Predict Words: Possible responses: **1.** fast; far **2.** fun **3.** four; five

Unit 3: No Time

Talk about the Story: 1. Possible responses: lazy; a procrastinator; messy **2.** Tess had no time to clean up only because she wasted her time.

Letters and Sounds: 3a. yes: tent **3b.** no: fan **3c.** yes: tape

Predict Words: 1. tell **2.** two; ten; twenty **3.** Take

Unit 4: A Bad Dream

Talk about the Story: 1. Possible responses: happy; relieved; scared **2.** Bud's dream is bad because Bud gets scared when his wife wants to use a hammer to break the jar off his hand.

Letters and Sounds: 3a. no: mouse **3b.** yes: box **3c.** yes: belt

Predict Words: Possible responses: **1.** bus; bike **2.** back **3.** best

Unit 5: Lost and Found

Talk about the Story: 1. silly; happy; relieved **2.** Lin thought she lost her glasses, but she found them on her head.

Letters and Sounds: 3a. yes: lamp **3b.** no: tap; faucet **3c.** yes: leaf

Predict Words: 1. like **2.** Leave **3.** live

Unit 6: My Dear Son

Talk about the Story: 1. a good father; patient; understanding; loving **2.** Dan drives his dad crazy, but his dad still loves him.

Letters and Sounds: 3a. yes: dice **3b.** yes: door **3c.** no: bird

Predict Words: 1. down **2.** dance **3.** date

Unit 7: A Nice Day

Talk about the Story: 1. Possible response: Nan will remember the note because it was a surprise that made her happy. **2.** Nan's bad day turns into a nice day because of the note.

Letters and Sounds: 3a. yes: nine **3b.** yes: nose **3c.** no: boots

Predict Words: 1. November **2.** night **3.** name

Unit 8: Pay Day

Talk about the Story: 1. Possible response: Yes, because the money Pam found was money Pam did not expect to have, so she used it to treat herself. **2.** Pam found money as she was washing clothes, so it was like being paid for her work.

Letters and Sounds: 3a. no: lion **3b.** yes: pen **3c.** yes: pot

Predict Words: 1. pans **2.** print **3.** post

Unit 9: Bus Stop

Talk about the Story: 1. Possible response: They want time to talk to each other. **2.** Possible responses: The story takes place at a bus stop. The man and woman meet at the bus stop.

Letters and Sounds: 3a. yes: sink **3b.** no: ball **3c.** yes: salt

Predict Words: 1. Sunday; Saturday **2.** soup; salad **3.** say

Unit 10: Holey Socks

Talk about the Story: 1. Hal was too excited about the sales. **2.** Hal's main goal was to buy socks because his socks had holes in them. But Hal ended up with holey socks.

Letters and Sounds: 3a. yes: house; home **3b.** yes: hand **3c.** no: dog

Predict Words: 1. How **2.** hear **3.** help